The Bear & The Butterfly
little ponderings

Written and Illustrated by
Mariella Travis

Alleiram Studios

Published by:
Mariella Travis
Alleiram Studios
Newburyport, MA 01950

Hardback - First Edition 2019

ISBN- 978-1-7341091-6-0

Alleiram Studios

www.alleiramstudios.com
mariella@alleiramstudios.com

For Mama
Thank you for always guiding me to spread my wings,
listen to my heart, and follow my inner light.

A seed is never stuck in the soil;
it is
g r o w i n g.
Have faith in the dirt, rain, and
sunlight that nourish you to
b l o o m .

Blessed
are we, to coexist with the
creatures of this earth.

Kindness and *respect* are the only
ways in which they are to be
treated.

The differences between
f l o w e r s
is what brings beauty to the
g a r d e n ...

...The differences between
u s
is what brings beauty to the
w o r l d .

In the
stillness of our minds,
we can hear the
symphony of our souls.

L i f e
is
a b u n d a n t
when seen with eyes of
g r a t i t u d e .

The
w o r l d
eagerly awaits the priceless
g i f t s
you have to share.

When soul is
p r e s e n t ,
fear is
a b s e n t .

Where you are is where
you are meant to be.
You are a blossom,
a spark about to grow into a
f l a m e .

Cultivate the power, light,
and joy within you,
and life will align to your
p u r p o s e .

We each hold a
m i r r o r
to the world.
Everyone we meet is a
reflection of
o u r s e l v e s .

It is our choice
whether or not to see a
s m i l e .
upon its surface.

It's okay to feel sad.

All emotions have
something to say;
one just has to
l i s t e n .

In presence of
m i n d
we find ourselves
s e e k i n g ...

...In presence of
h e a r t
we find ourselves
b e i n g .

You
are a
masterpiece!

Sometimes, it is in
solitude and silence
that the universe shares its
greatest secrets.

No need to care about
messy hair,
perfection, or
"just right";
for you, my dear,
with eyes so clear, are
beautiful, brave, and bright!

Sometimes, life creates
s t o r m s
to bring clarity of mind;
cleansing the soul
so your heart can
s h i n e .

The greatest form of
b e a u t y
is the
l i g h t
that you hold.

Disagreements are
opportunities
to understand, love, and
speak how you
feel .

Warmth of heart,
warmth of soul;
In every season
your beauty shows.
Whether sun or whether snow,
in every season
your beauty grows.

Breathe
a little deeper,
and you'll see the world
around you with greater
clarity.

It's okay to feel
u n c e r t a i n ,
it's okay to feel
u n s u r e .
Deep breaths and
a hug or two,
many times are the best
c u r e .

Leave only
f o o t p r i n t s
and a trail of
j o y
behind you.

You are
blessed
you are
loved
you are
free
you are
safe

All around and above in this
heavenly place.

My deepest gratitude to:

Mama
For your infinite encouragement.
"Finish your idea, then you can go to bed."
No matter how late, or early, the hours go!

Dad
For your sense of humor.
And no, despite the endless dad-jokes, I would rather you not be boring!

Grannie Annie
For your joy in my creations, constructive thoughts, and ideas.

Manny
For your care and inspirational words of wisdom.

Shehroz
For your love and excitement in my potential.

Bridget
For your listening ear and pure heart.

Thank you to all who helped bring this book into creation.